John Taylor's
RUGBY QUIZ BOOK

John Taylor's
RUGBY QUIZ BOOK

A Graham Tarrant Book
David & Charles
Newton Abbot London North Pomfret (Vt)

All photographs by Colin Elsey/Colorsport

British Library Cataloguing in Publication Data

Taylor, John, *1942–*
 John Taylor's rugby quiz book. –
 (A Graham Tarrant book).
 1. Rugby football – Miscellanea
 I. Title
 796.33'3'076   GV945.2

ISBN 0–7153–8946–7

Phototypeset by Northern Phototypesetting Co, Bolton
and printed in Great Britain
by Billings & Sons Ltd, Worcester
for David & Charles Publishers plc
Brunel House Newton Abbot Devon

Published in the United States of America
by David & Charles Inc
North Pomfret Vermont 05053 USA

CONTENTS

INTRODUCTION

The Welsh national newspaper, *The Western Mail*, still claim their most common enquiry on anything is, 'Who dropped the last four-point goal for Wales?' and generally in the sporting world the fascination with who did what, where and when seems to grow. Games such as cricket have always attracted the statistics nut, but now with the proliferation of sports quiz games on TV, radio and in the local pub, the budding memory man needs a bible of trivia in every sport.

This little volume includes most of the straightforward rugby records, some of the more unusual feats and some real mind-benders for which I make no apology, having been on the receiving end of some of them for the last twenty years.

No doubt Ellis Wyn Williams, the resident question master at London Welsh, will be disappointed that his old favourites – 'Name five Welsh internationals with no vowels in their surnames' and 'Name a Welsh team of Williamses all playing in their right positions (and you can use JPR as a flanker)' – are missing; but I have tried not to be too obscure. For example, where a question asks what was 'unique' or 'unusual' about a player it does relate absolutely to rugby and not the fact that he was the only known phrenologist to score five tries against France on a Friday.

Researching the book gave me a great deal of fun, and put right a few mistaken beliefs as well. I hope it does the same for you. All answers are correct at 1 January 1987.

By the way, Willie Davies scored the last four-point dropped goal for Wales in 1939. The vowel-less Welsh internationals were two Gwynns, two Blyths and a Skrym. You can work out the Williamses for yourselves.

My thanks to just about every author who has written a book on rugby – I think I have delved into most – and particularly to Chris Rhys, who was a constant source of the unusual and also corrected my mistakes – I hope.

John Taylor

England

1 In which International Board country have England never won an international?

2 Who is England's most-capped player?

3 England's biggest winning margin and highest score were both achieved before the first world war. Which country were they against, and what were the scores?

4 D. Lambert of Harlequins made a remarkable debut for England in 1907. Why?

5 How many times have England won the Grand Slam?

6 England's biggest losing margin and highest number of points conceded were both in the same match. They lost 15–42. When, where and against whom?

7 Nine Smiths have played for England. Which other surname is shared by nine England players?

8 England have beaten the All Blacks only once in New Zealand. When was it and what made the victory even more remarkable?

9 Why is Jamie Salmon unique amongst modern England internationals?

10 Who was England's most-capped player before the second world war?

11 England once scored 13 tries in an international. Who against, where and when?

12 John Pullin, England's most-capped hooker, achieved another unique distinction. What was it?

13 Only one England back has won more than 30 caps in the same position. Who is he?

14 When did England last beat Wales in Cardiff, and who was the English captain?

15 How many scrum-halves played for England while Gareth Edwards played 53 consecutive times for Wales, between 1967 and 1978?

16 England have beaten which International Board country more than 50 times?

17 Which was the most successful decade in English rugby?

18 The longest international career for an English player spanned 13 seasons. Who was he and how many caps did he win?

19 Who holds the English record for the highest number of points scored in internationals, and what is his total?

20 Name the player who scored tries in both England games on the 1985 tour to New Zealand.

21 Who was the player who scored two tries for England on his debut in 1986?

22 England gave first caps to two Wasps' players against Wales in 1984. One was Paul Rendall. Who was the other?

23 Who was the only player to appear in all of England's 12 games during the 1984/85 and 1985/86 seasons?

24 In 1984 this man became only the fourth player to captain England on his international debut.

25 When he appeared as replacement against France in 1983 he became the first player to appear three times as a substitute for England.

26 Name the player who has captained England on a record 19 occasions.

27 Who scored England's only try in the 15–9 victory against New Zealand in 1983?

28 Prior to Bill Beaumont in 1980, who was the last England player to captain the Lions on tour?

29 Two players made their England debut in the Centenary match against the President's XV. One was Peter Dixon who went on to win 22 caps. Who was the other debutant who won his only cap in that game?

30 During England's 1980 Grand Slam campaign they beat France 17–13 in Paris. Who was the player who scored two drop goals in the match?

Answers on p. 69

Family Ties

1 He was captain of South Africa in the 1980 series against the Lions, his father captained South Africa in 1949 against New Zealand. Who are they?

2 In 1964, playing for Australia against New Zealand, they became the only twin brothers to play together in international rugby.

3 Name the player who came on as a replacement for his injured brother against Wales in 1970.

4 One brother played seven games for Scotland in 1977–8, the other in two Tests for South Africa v the 1974 Lions.

5 During the West Midlands v Australians game in 1967, who were the brothers who appeared on opposite sides?

6 On the final game of their British tour of 1963–4, New Zealand beat the Barbarians 36–3. Who were the brothers who appeared on opposite sides?

7 Name the only British Lion who was the son of another British Lion.

8 Brothers – one of whom was playing Test cricket for England on the same day that the other was playing rugby for England against Scotland.

9 Brothers – one of whom played in Scotland's back row in 1986, while the other played 27 times in Scotland's back row between 1981 and 1985.

10 When Australia toured the British Isles in 1981–2 they included the brothers, Glen, Gary and Mark Ella. They also included a pair of cousins. Can you name them?

11 During the late 1970s and early 1980s, Leicester dominated English club rugby. Who were the brothers who propped Peter Wheeler in their front row?

12 Who were the New Zealand brothers who both appeared against Australia in 1984 and 1985?

All Blacks v Wallabies

1 For the second Test against Australia in 1982, New Zealand recalled a former All Black who had been playing club rugby in England since 1978. Who was he?

2 In addition to losing a series in Australia for the first time since 1934, the 1980 All Blacks were also beaten by a State side. They went down 9–3 against which team?

3 Who captained New Zealand on that ill-fated tour to Australia in 1980?

4 Australia's first win against New Zealand in 45 years was achieved with a 12–6 victory at Sydney in 1979. Paul McLean kicked three penalties for Australia, but which player dropped a crucial goal?

5 On the New Zealand tour to Australia and Fiji in 1974, who was the player who scored 13 tries including four in the 117–6 win against South Australia?

6 In 1972 New Zealand beat Australia 29–6, 30–17 and 38–3 in a three-match series. Three players scored tries in all three matches. Bryan Williams and Ian Kirkpatrick were two – who was the third?

7 Who was Australia's tour captain when they visited New Zealand in 1962?

8 Who was the player who scored eight tries when New Zealand beat Northern New South Wales 103–0 in 1962. He went on to score 14 tries in seven games on the tour?

9 After 13 straight victories in Australia in 1957, the New Zealand team were beaten 11–9 by which side in the final game of the tour?

10 The 1924–5 All Blacks made a 38 match tour to Australia, the British Isles, France and Canada. They won 36 games, losing only one. Who did they lose it against?

11 New Zealand won all 12 matches on the tour to Australia and Fiji in 1968. Which player scored 120 points in 10 games during the tour?

Answers on pp. 71–2

Ireland

1 Three Irishmen have played more than 60 times for their country. Who are they?

2 Ireland have won the Grand Slam on only one occasion. When was it and who was their captain?

3 Who is Ireland's most-capped outside-half?

4 Which International Board country have Ireland never beaten?

5 Who has scored most tries for Ireland in internationals?

6 Who did Ireland beat by a record score in November 1986?

7 Which Irishman went on four consecutive Lions' tours to South Africa?

8 Which player has twice scored 21 points in a Home International Championship match?

9 C. M. H. Gibson is the world's most-capped player. What are his christian names?

10 How many times have Ireland won the Triple Crown?

11 Ireland have more wins than losses against only one International Board country. Which one?

12 Which is the most common surname shared by Irish internationals?

13 What was unique about the Ireland v Wales match in 1887?

14 Why did Ireland play only two Championship matches in 1972?

15 Ireland have played all but two of their Home Internationals against England in Dublin. Where were the others played?

16 Is it true that Ireland have supplied an outside-half for every Lions' tour since the second world war?

17 Tony Ward played soccer for which club in a major European competition?

18 He played in 28 internationals between 1955 and 1963 and was then called up as a last-minute replacement against England in 1970. Who is he?

19 Ireland lost all four Championship games in 1986, but one player scored in three of the four games. Who was he?

20 Which Irishman made a record 17 appearances in Test matches for the British Lions?

21 Who became the most-capped prop ever in the 1986–7 season?

22 Which Irish club is the country's oldest?

23 Name the Irish province which beat Australia 11–8 in 1967, New Zealand 12–0 in 1978 and Australia 15–6 in 1981.

24 Who captained Ireland on 24 occasions between 1963 and 1973?

25 During the 1985–6 season, which Irish club remained unbeaten throughout their 28 match programme?

26 Although the Lions were beaten 26–22 in the first Test against South Africa in 1980, an Irish player set a new record by scoring 18 points in the match. Who was he?

27 What does CIYMS stand for?

28 Brendan Mullin is the Irish record-holder for which track event?

29 In which city is the Dolphin club based?

30 J. J. Moloney won 27 caps in all. 23 were at scrum-half – where were the other four?

Answers on pp. 73–4

Nicknames

Name the following players:

1 Shadow

2 Majid

3 Basil Brush

4 Monsieur 'Le Drop'

5 Bébé

6 Papa

7 Boss

8 Straw man

9 Wheelbrace

10 Cowboy

11 Pole

12 Grizz

13 Stookie

14 Mighty Mouse (give his christened name)

15 The Bear

16 Boy

17 Flappie

18 Flippie

19 Wild Bill

20 Nipper

21 Awesome Aub

22 Cuckoo

23 Wilder

24 Trout

Answers on p. 75

The Name's the Same

Each of the following pairs of rugby players share the same surname. Can you identify both players in each case?

1 Scorer of probably the most famous 'non-try' in the history of games between Wales and New Zealand – and the name of Scotland's most-capped hooker.

2 Forward who played in New Zealand's four victories over the 1983 British Lions – and captain of Australia's touring team to the British Isles in 1981–2.

3 England's replacement scrum-half for the injured Nigel Melville in 1985 – and the captain of the 1908 Anglo–Welsh touring team to New Zealand.

4 England's most-capped scrum-half – and the captain of the 1962 British Lions in South Africa.

5 Player who made his 100th appearance for the All Blacks on their tour to Wales in 1980 – and the Scottish international who was later to become the BBC Rugby Correspondent.

6 Scorer of the record number of points on any international rugby tour – and the captain of the 'Waratahs', the New South Wales touring team to Britain in 1928.

7 He scored a record 36 points for England against Western Australia in 1975 – and the player who scored a record 166 points in international matches for Wales.

8 The name of the most-capped back of both Wales and New Zealand.

9 Captain of England's last Grand Slam winning team before Bill Beaumont's – and the scorer of a then record six penalty goals for Wales against France in 1982.

10 Successor to Jim Aitken as captain of Scotland – and the captain of New Zealand on their short tour to the

British Isles in 1974.

11 He was captain of England on their first tour of New Zealand – and the only West of Scotland player to be capped for England.

12 One of the greatest of all rugby players – and a namesake who played in the pack for Ireland.

Answers on pp. 76–7

Scotland

1 Which Scot has scored more points in major internationals than any other player in the world?

2 What less enviable world record is held by Roger Baird?

3 Scotland staged rugby's first-ever international match. Where did it take place and against whom?

4 What was Ned Haig's contribution to the game of rugby?

5 At the end of the 1986 season Scotland had an evenly balanced international record against which country?

6 Scotland featured in the highest scoring drawn international of all time. Which was the other country? In what year and what was the score?

7 How many times have Scotland won the Triple Crown and when did they last win it before 1984?

8 Ian McLauchlan, Ian Milne and Ian McGeechan have all played more than 30 times for Scotland. What else do they have in common?

9 What distinction did Scotland achieve at Hampden Park in 1906?

10 Who was the first replacement in international rugby?

11 Two Scots played for the British Lions when they won the Test series against New Zealand in 1971 and South Africa in 1974. Who were they?

12 Who is the only player to have scored four tries in an international on two occasions?

13 Who has scored most points for Scotland in a Home International Championship season?

14 What is the worst defeat ever suffered by Scotland?

15 Andy Irvine scored 56 points in New Zealand in 1981, equalling the record set on the 1970 tour to Australia. Who set it and for which club did he play?

16 R. M. Kinnear, who played three times for Scotland in 1926, is unique amongst Scottish internationals. Why?

17 Jim Aitken captained Scotland to their Grand Slam in 1984. Who captained them to their only other one in 1925?

18 Who was the Gala forward who captained Scotland to victory over England twice in eight days in 1971?

19 New Zealand completed their Grand Slam over the Home Countries with an 18–9 win over Scotland in 1978. Which player scored Scotland's first try against New Zealand in 43 years in that game?

20 In 1978 which player became the first to reach 50 caps for his country?

21 When Hawick won the 1985–6 Scottish Championship for the fourth successive year, they lost only one game. The team that beat them lost every other game. Name them.

22 Which player captained Scotland in a record 19 internationals?

23 In 1977 he won his first cap as a flank forward against England, then in 1986 he was recalled to win his fourth cap, also against England, but this time as a prop. Who is he?

24 Which brothers both played in Scotland's Championship side in 1979–80, but not together?

25 Having played eight times for Scotland between 1949 and 1953, he went on to manage the 1971 British Lions. Who is he?

26 Who is the player who won 44 caps for Scotland but was never selected for the Lions, thus becoming the most-capped non-Lion ever?

Answers on pp. 76–7

27 After Heriot's Former Pupils won the Middlesex Sevens in 1949, it was 33 years before another club from north of the border won the trophy. Which club?

28 Peter Dods scored 43 points in one match on a Scottish tour in 1985. Against whom?

29 Galashiels and Hawick have dominated the Scottish Club Championship, but which other club has won it?

30 Which club plays at Murrayfield?

All Rounders

Can you name the following:

1 He played in the 1902 FA Cup Final, won caps for England at soccer and cricket, and played rugby for Blackheath and the Barbarians.

2 An England international who captained the England cricket team on 25 occasions.

3 A Scottish international in 1922 and 1923, he went on to win a gold and bronze medal on the track at the 1924 Olympics.

4 An England international in the seventies who was also a member of the England Under 21 water polo team.

5 The Springbok fly-half of the thirties who played Test cricket after the war and was also a hockey international.

6 The Welsh international who won Junior Wimbledon.

7 Another Welshman who broke the UK Junior 200 yards hurdles record in 1966 in the heats of the English Schools Championships, beating Alan Pascoe by 20 yards.

8 The scorer of the last-minute penalty which enabled New Zealand to beat Wales in 1978, who was also the recipient of the underarm ball bowled by Trevor Chappell in a One Day International cricket match.

9 He played for England v Ireland in 1947, and went on to score a century for New Zealand at Lords against England in 1949.

10 The English and Welsh internationals who ran for Great Britain in the 4 x 100 metres relay in the 1948 Olympics.

11 The member of the Pontypool front row who was also a judo Black Belt.

12 Having played four internationals for England in 1949, he returned to South Africa and played 19 times for them at cricket.

13 He played for Ireland against Australia in 1947, having won 10 Republic of Ireland soccer caps between 1933 and 1947.

14 Between 1885 and 1898 he played for England on 10 occasions at rugby and 16 times at cricket.

15 This England captain played 13 internationals between 1890 and 1895, then played 3 cricket Tests for England and 3 more for Australia.

16 The All Black who played in 32 Tests between 1977 and 1984, who won a bronze medal for wrestling in the 1974 Commonwealth Games.

17 He captained Dorset and Wilts and won a Cambridge blue before giving up rugby to train Derby winner, Mill Reef, and the Queen's horses.

18 He won the sprint double in the 1938 Empire Games and played three times on the wing for England. Who was he?

19 Who was the Springbok wing who in 1986 was South African record holder for the 400 metres with a world-class time of 45.01 seconds?

20 England rugby internationals Alistair Hignell and Rob Andrew share a rare distinction. What is it?

County Championship

1 In 1985–6 they made their first appearance in the final of the competition since beating Leicestershire in 1927, but lost 16–6 against Warwickshire.

2 Which team reached the final of the competition for the first time ever in 1984–5, before losing 12–9 against Middlesex?

3 Who was the player who, in the 1985–6 final, scored a championship record three pushover tries?

4 In 1966–7 Surrey drew 14–14 and then nil–nil in the replay to become joint champions with which county – the only time the title has been shared?

5 Between 1958 and 1965 Warwickshire won seven of the eight finals. Which side beat Devon 5–3 in the 1961 final replay after a nil–nil draw?

6 Which player made his last appearance for Lancashire in their 7–3 win over N. Midlands in the 1981–2 final?

7 Which county appeared in 12 finals between 1970 and 1984?

8 Lancashire played three finals at home between 1974 and 1980. Two of the games were played at Blundellsands, but on which ground did they beat Gloucestershire in 1980?

9 Which county became champions for the first and to date only time after beating Gloucestershire 11–9 in the 1970 final?

10 Who was the player who scored all 24 points when his side beat Middlesex 24–9 at Richmond in the 1976 final?

11 Coventry provided 13 players for the victorious Warwickshire team in the 1985–6 final. Name the two clubs who provided the other two players?

12 Which side beat Gloucestershire 10–7 in the 1978 final, to achieve their only victory in the competition to date?

25

Answers on pp. 80–1

Wales

1 Who has scored most points in internationals for Wales?

2 Which player captained Wales on most occasions?

3 Four Welshmen played in internationals both before and after the second world war. Who were they?

4 Graham Price, Bobby Windsor and Charlie Faulkner achieved a unique double together. What was it?

5 A second-row pairing for Wales who both won their first international caps for the British Lions. Who are they?

6 Who equalled the Welsh points scoring record playing out of position in his first international at the age of 18.

7 Wales have won the Triple Crown more than any other country. How many times?

8 Two Welshmen have twice scored two tries in Test matches for the British Lions. Name them.

9 Who is Wales's most-capped outside-half?

10 Who played in every position behind the scrum except scrum-half?

11 Which is the commonest surname shared by Welsh internationals?

12 Which International Board country have Wales never beaten?

13 When was the last international played at Swansea, and who was it against?

14 Which two players jointly hold the Welsh try-scoring record?

15 Bleddyn Williams won his first cap in which year, and at what position?

16 Why was Charlie Faulkner the odd man out in the Pontypool front row?

17 Barry John still holds one international record. What is it?

18 What record did Wales achieve in the 1975–6 season?

19 A Welshman holds the world record for the number of conversions in one international. Who is he?

20 In the 1985–6 International Championship, who kicked a penalty goal from almost 71 yards?

21 Geoff Wheel was the first Welsh player to be sent off in an international. Who was the second?

22 Who was the player who captained Wales on his international debut against England in 1963?

23 J. P. R. Williams won 55 caps for Wales. He won 54 caps as a fullback. In which position did he win the fifty-fifth cap?

24 Who was the first Welshman after World War II to captain the British Lions on an overseas tour?

25 Who captained Wales to a 40–3 victory against Fiji at Cardiff in 1985–6?

26 Playing for Llanelli between 1965 and 1979 this player scored a world record 312 tries in 454 games – a record which stood until broken by Bristol's Alan Morley. Who is he?

27 How does a player win the Lloyd Lewis Memorial Trophy?

28 On New Zealand's tour to Britain and France in 1963–4, they lost only one game. Who were the team that took their unbeaten record?

29 At Twickenham in 1970 England led Wales 13–6 with only 13 minutes remaining, when Gareth Edwards was injured. Who was the player who replaced Edwards, to win his only cap and inspire Wales to a 17–13 victory?

Answers on pp. 80–1

30 Graham Price scored a famous try on his Welsh debut in the 25–10 win against France in Paris in 1975. But which other Welshman also scored a try on his debut in the same game?

Captains

Name the players who captained the following sides:

1 Japan against England at Twickenham in 1986.

2 Cardiff to victory in the 1985–6 Schweppes Challenge Cup final.

3 Hawick to the Scottish Division One Championship in 1985–6.

4 Warwickshire to a 16–6 victory against Kent in the 1986 County Championship final.

5 England on their 1985 tour to New Zealand.

6 Scotland on their 1985 tour to North America.

7 France in their joint championship season of 1985–6.

8 New Zealand on tour to Wales and North America in 1980.

9 Australia's Grand Slam winning tour of the British Isles in 1984.

10 The All Blacks in their 2–1 series defeat by Australia in 1986?

11 Ireland to a 2–0 Test series victory in Australia in 1979.

12 Wales to Australia on the 1978 tour.

13 The British Lions in New Zealand and Fiji in 1983.

14 The British Lions in South Africa in 1974.

15 Leicester in 1985–6.

16 Selkirk in 1985–6.

17 Pontypool in 1985–6.

18 The Overseas Unions in their 32–13 victory over a Five Nations XV at Twickenham in 1986.

19 The Rest in their 15–7 victory over the British Lions at Cardiff in 1986.

20 Oxford University in the 1985 Varsity Match.

All Blacks v Springboks

1 Clive Norling refereed the second and third Tests between New Zealand and South Africa in 1981, but who was the Englishman who took charge of the first Test?

2 After both sides had won one Test in 1981, New Zealand beat South Africa 25–22 at Auckland in the final match to take the series 2–1. However which South African scored a hat-trick of tries in that final Test?

3 South Africa won the second Test of the 1981 series against New Zealand 24–12. Alan Hewson scored all New Zealand's points, but who scored 20 points for South Africa?

4 Who was tour captain of New Zealand on their 1976 visit to South Africa?

5 Despite being overlooked for selection in all four Tests, he scored 132 points for New Zealand in 11 games on the 1976 tour to South Africa. Who was he?

6 On their tour to South Africa in 1970, New Zealand won 23 of their 26 games, but lost the Test series 3–1. Against which side did Gerald Kember score 34 points in an 85–0 victory?

7 Who was the loose forward who scored tries in each of the first three Tests for New Zealand against South Africa in 1965, New Zealand eventually winning the series 3–1?

8 South Africa beat New Zealand 2–1 in 1960, with one Test being drawn. Who captained South Africa to their series victory?

9 Who was the South African player who scored all fifteen points when South Africa beat New Zealand 15–11 in 1949, then went on to score 89 points on South Africa's tour to the UK in 1951–2?

10 When South Africa toured New Zealand for the first time in 1921, they were captained in the Tests by tour vice-captain 'Boy' Morkel. Who was the tour captain who

31

Answers on p. 83

did not play in the Tests and never appeared in an international?

11 Tour Captain Wynand Claassen did not play in the first Test of South Africa's 1981 series in New Zealand. Who was the player who took Claassen's No 8 position in the 14–9 defeat in Christchurch?

12 Who was the player who scored a record 175 points in only 12 matches on New Zealand's tour to South Africa in 1960?

France

1 France did not play in the Five Nations Championship between 1931 and 1939. Why?

2 Which French player holds the record for the highest number of points scored in one Five Nations Championship season?

3 Altogether four players have kicked three drop goals in an international. Who are the two Frenchmen to have done so?

4 What record do P. Estève and P. Sella share?

5 France has beaten New Zealand five times in 21 matches, but only once in New Zealand. When was it and who was captain?

6 Who is France's most-capped player?

7 Name the two players who were almost interchangeable as No 8 in the late sixties and early seventies?

8 Who was the French fullback who became the National Coach of Italy?

9 France did not record a win in two of the Home Countries until after the second world war. Which were they?

10 When did France become the eighth member nation of the International Board?

11 In what country was Serge Blanco born?

12 France created three national points-scoring records in the 1985–6 Five Nations Championship and equalled another. What were they?

13 What is the link between W. J. Whineray of New Zealand and J. P. Rives?

14 Three sets of brothers have played together for France

since 1960. Who are they?

15 In what year did France first play all four Home Countries to make it the Five Nations Championship?

16 When did France first win the Championship outright and who was captain?

17 Who captained France to their second Grand Slam in 1977?

18 Which international rugby organisation did France help to found in 1934?

19 Which club has won the French Championship on most occasions?

20 Which non-IB country beat France for the first time in 1985?

21 Which player scored a try after a quick line-out in the first minute of the game against Scotland at Murrayfield in 1986?

22 Who scored two drop goals on his debut against Ireland in 1981, and added two more in the next away match against England?

23 Who was the first French player to win 50 caps? He achieved it against Wales in 1972.

24 When France beat England 13–0 in 1962, which player became the first forward to score three tries in a championship game?

25 For which French team did Englishman Nigel Horton play after leaving Moseley?

26 Jean-Pierre Rives began his career with Stade Toulousain, but with which club did he finish it?

27 Which French tournament, second only in importance to the Club Championship, is named after one of its greatest players?

28 Jean-Patrick Lescarboura twice scored 17 points in a

Five Nations Match in 1984. Who emulated him two years later?

29 Which Prime Minister, Head of State and Lord Mayor of Paris won two caps in 1945?

30 Which club provided seven members of the French team for an international in 1984?

British Lions

1 What record was established by James Frederick Byrne on the Lions' tour to South Africa in 1896?

2 The 1924 Lions were crippled with injuries and they sent out an SOS for an ex-Irish international living in Johannesburg. Who was this Irishman who became a Lion without being selected for the tour party, or being sent out from the Home Countries?

3 A 'mini' Lions' tour in 1927, with players selected from England, Ireland and Scotland, achieved 'Test' victories of 37–0, 46–0, 34–3 and 43–0 against which country?

4 The last of the pre-second world war rugby tours was the British Lions to South Africa in 1938. Who was the Irishman who captained the side?

5 The first Lions' tour after the second world war was to New Zealand and Australia in 1950. This team was also captained by an Irishman. Who was he?

6 He arrived for a Lions' tour with his arm in plaster and did not make his first appearance until the eighteenth game of the tour. Twenty-one years later he managed one of the most famous of all Lions teams. Who was he?

7 Who scored a hat-trick of tries for South Africa in the second Test against the 1955 Lions? He later joined St Helens Rugby League club.

8 When New Zealand had a 4–0 series victory against the 1966 Lions, who was the player who scored a total of 87 points – only two points adrift of Don Clarke's 1959 record?

9 Which player in 1968 withdrew from the Lions' party with injury prior to the departure from Britain, but was later flown out as a replacement?

10 Lewis Jones achieved two notable firsts when he joined the 1950 Lions' tour to New Zealand and Australia – what were they?

11 Why does G. W. Lee of Rockliff hold a special place in Lions' tour history?

12 Who was the first Lion to score two tries in a Test match?

13 Fifty-five seconds against Eastern Province in the opening game of the 1980 tour of South Africa was the length of his Lions' career.

14 He scored 100 points on two successive Lions' tours and yet he was never chosen to play for the Lions in a Test.

15 Scorer of eight tries for the Lions on the 1974 tour of South Africa, although a second-row forward.

16 A replacement on the 1983 tour to New Zealand, he scored two tries in two appearances before injury ended his tour.

17 Which Lions' captain joined Warrington Rugby League club on returning home?

18 Captain of the Lions in the 1986 International Board Centenary game against The Rest at Cardiff.

19 He became the first player to tour Australia at both Rugby Union and Rugby League with teams representing Great Britain.

20 On which Lions' tour have there been most replacements so far, and how many were needed to stem the injury tide?

21 Two different players with the same name (surname *and* Christian name) who went on successive Lions' tours.

22 Which player has won most Test caps for the Lions?

23 Name the two players who have scored six tries in a provincial game for the Lions.

24 On the 1983 tour to New Zealand, Hugo MacNeill played fullback in two of the four Tests. Who played fullback in the other two?

Answers on p. 88

Off You Go

1 As a result of biting the ear of Oxford University prop Ollie Waldron, this Australian hooker was sent home from the 1966 tour.

2 Playing for Moseley against Gloucester in the inaugural English Cup Final in 1972, he became the first player to be sent off at Twickenham in 47 years.

3 Australian wing-threequarter who was sent off against Swansea during the 1975–6 tour of the British Isles.

4 In 1925 this man created history by becoming the first player sent off in international rugby, and also the first to be dismissed at Twickenham.

5 Playing against East Transvaal in 1968, he became the first British Lion to be sent off anywhere.

6 Who was the All Black sent home from the 1972–3 tour of the British Isles as a disciplinary measure after violent scenes at a Cardiff hotel?

7 Who was the referee who sent Paul Ringer from the field at Twickenham in the England v Wales game of 1980?

8 During the second Test at Brisbane against Australia, he became the first England player to be sent off in an international.

9 The Australians beat the Midlands 21–18 at Leicester, but the result was overshadowed by the sending off of which two players?

10 Both Geoff Wheel and Willie Duggan were sent off during the Wales v Ireland game at Cardiff in 1977. Who was the referee who took the decision?

11 Who was the first Frenchman to be sent off in an international?

12 Who was the Scottish player involved in the incident in the Scotland v New Zealand game in 1967 which resulted in Colin Meads being dismissed from the field by Kevin Kelleher?

Answers on p. 89

The Changing Game

1 Which country delayed, for four years, a move at the turn of the century to introduce uniform scoring?

2 Which method of scoring ceased to exist when the free kick clause was introduced in 1977?

3 Who was the first player to score a try worth four points in an international?

4 Which was the first Welsh club to celebrate its centenary?

5 When the first uniform rules were eventually agreed upon in the 1890–1 season, how many points were awarded for a try?

6 Which famous novel of the 1850s includes a vivid account of the game of rugby?

7 Who were the first official manufacturers of rugby balls for the Rugby Union, they too being based in Rugby?

8 Which player recorded the first four-point try in the Five Nations championship?

9 In which year were replacements first allowed in a Five Nations Championship match?

10 When was the 'Australian dispensation' rule first applied in the Five Nations Championship?

11 In what year was the drop goal revalued to be worth three points. What was it worth before that, and who scored the first three-point drop goal in an international?

12 On how many occasions did rugby feature in the Olympic Games?

13 In which year was the Rugby League founded?

14 In which year was the number of players in a team reduced to 15, and how many players had been allowed in

each team prior to that?

15 Rugby was first introduced to Japan in: a) 1897 b) 1922 c) 1946?

16 How was the 1984 French Championship final decided?

17 What major change in formation was adopted by New Zealand in 1932?

18 In what year was Twickenham first used for an international, and what was it before it became Rugby's HQ?

19 Before 1958 a player was not allowed to pick up the ball directly after a tackle – what was he required to do?

20 Again in 1958 there was a major change relating to place-kicking. What was it?

Answers on pp. 90–1

New Zealand

1 Only one All Blacks team has a perfect record on a long tour of the UK. Which one?

2 New Zealand have never lost to which two International Board countries?

3 Two New Zealand records date back to the 1905–6 tour of the British Isles and France. What are they?

4 Two All Blacks lead the table for the most points scored in one international match. Name them.

5 Name the three players who hold the world record for appearances at international level as a front-row combination.

6 Who is New Zealand's most-capped player?

7 In the famous 1905 international against Wales, who thought he had scored a match-saving try?

8 Which country has clocked up the most victories in matches between New Zealand and South Africa?

9 Who holds the points-scoring record in internationals for New Zealand?

10 Who set a world record for the highest number of points scored by an individual in a touring match, against South Australia in 1984?

11 Who is New Zealand's most-capped back?

12 Which was the first New Zealand province to beat a British Isles' touring team?

13 When did B. J. Lochore win his last cap, and in what circumstances?

14 When Stu Wilson broke the New Zealand try-scoring record he did it in style. How, against whom, and what is his total number of international tries?

15 Only one New Zealand team has failed to win a Test on a tour of the UK. Which one?

16 Which All Black has good reason to be grateful for the medical skills of Dr J. P. R. Williams?

17 Have New Zealand ever won an international series in South Africa?

18 Which New Zealand player broke his jaw on both his tours to the UK?

19 Which team stopped the 1967 All Blacks from winning every game in Britain?

20 Who captained the All Blacks in the 1971 home series against the British Lions?

21 When New Zealand beat England 18–13 at Christchurch in 1985, which player scored all 18 of New Zealand's points?

22 Which provincial side resisted 25 successive challenges for the Ranfurly Shield between 1960 and 1963, and which province equalled that record between 1982 and 1985?

23 Who was the player who scored 46 points for New Zealand in the four Tests against the 1983 British Lions?

24 Between 1966 and 1978, who was the player who appeared in 11 Tests for the British Lions against New Zealand?

25 Against which team did the touring All Blacks run up a 117–6 scoreline in 1974?

26 When New Zealand beat Ireland 10–6 in Dublin in 1978, which player scored two drop goals?

27 Who was the New Zealand captain who scored the final try when his side beat the Barbarians 36–3 at Cardiff in 1964?

28 During the famous All Black v Barbarians match at Cardiff in 1973, who was the New Zealand player who

scored two tries?

29 The 1983 All Black tour to England and Scotland was hastily arranged to replace another tour. Which country were New Zealand originally supposed to visit?

30 Stu Wilson scored his fiftieth try for the All Blacks on the 1983 tour and retired from international rugby at the end of it. Apart from not winning a Test, he created a 'first' as captain. What was it?

Places of Interest

1 What was the venue for the first match in the International Championship?

2 Where was the 1962 County Championship final between Warwickshire and Hampshire played?

3 England last played a home international match at a venue other than Twickenham in 1923, when they played Ireland at which ground?

4 Which team played at St Michaels until 1986?

5 At which ground was the highest score involving two International Board countries recorded in 1910?

6 Where did England play their first home game in the International Championship?

7 Which English club plays its home matches at Webb Ellis Road?

8 Where was the Varsity Match played between 1887 and 1920?

9 The record paying attendance for a rugby international is 104,000, established in 1975. Where?

10 Scotland built the first 'purpose built' stadium for international matches in 1899. It was in Edinburgh, but what was it called?

11 New Zealand's first home international was against the British Isles at Athletic Park, Wellington. The second was in Dunedin – what was the name of the ground?

12 In 1928 when New Zealand first toured South Africa two of the Tests were played in Durban and Port Elizabeth. What were the names of the grounds?

Firsts

1 Which was the first senior Rugby Union club in Wales?

2 What first took place at Cambridge, Massachusetts, in 1976?

3 Which country did Australia play for the first time in an international in 1976?

4 For which trophy did New Zealand and Australia first compete in 1931?

5 Gloucestershire suffered their first home defeat in the County Championship for seven years in the 1978 semi-final. Who beat them?

6 Who were the first beaten finalists in the John Player Cup?

7 Who was the first Scot to captain the British Lions?

8 Which was the first British side, in 1957, to play in Moscow?

9 Who were the first Olympic rugby champions?

10 Who was the first player from any IB country to win 50 caps?

11 Which team played in Britain for the first time in 1977?

12 Who were the first winners of the Grand Slam?

13 Name the two countries that took part in the first televised Rugby Union match on 19 March 1938?

14 Who captained the very first British Isles tourists to Australia and New Zealand?

15 Which hospital, in 1841, formed the first ever Rugby Union club?

16 Which famous player was the first Rugby Union

international to lose his life during World War II?

17 The first floodlit rugby match took place on 22 October 1878 and involved two teams that joined the Northern Union in 1895. Name either.

18 What Rugby Union 'first' was achieved by John Birkett of Harlequins against Richmond in October 1909?

19 Who was the first man to captain England at both rugby and cricket?

20 Which was the first Welsh club to beat two international touring teams in one year?

21 Who was the first player to appear in both an English and Welsh Cup final?

22 In the 1970s, which country became the first to win the Grand Slam using the same 15 players in all four games?

23 The same player scored the last four-point dropped goal and the first three-point dropped goal for England. Who was he?

24 Which was the first (and so far the only) international touring team to go through a series against the four Home Countries without conceding a try, and in which season did it happen?

Australia

Continued on p. 57

1 Which family has supplied six internationals spread over three generations to the national team?

2 Who is the former Wasps' player who holds the record for appearances in the second-row against International Board countries?

3 Australia beat three of the four Home Countries by record margins during their Grand Slam in 1984. Which was the odd one out?

4 Name the Australian international who won 30 caps in the forties and fifties who went on to become Lord Mayor of Sydney?

5 Australia have only beaten the British Lions once. In which year?

6 Why did Graham Price leave the field in the second Test against Australia in 1978?

7 Australia once scored six tries in an international. Against whom and when?

8 What was unique about the Test series between Australia and South Africa in 1933?

9 Who has won more Tests in South Africa – Australia or New Zealand?

10 When did Australia last beat South Africa in Australia?

11 He won 34 caps at scrum-half between 1968 and 1982. Who is he?

12 The 1908 Wallabies beat Cornwall 32–3. What was the special significance of that result?

13 What is the name of the cup for which Australia and New Zealand compete?

14 Which Australian tourists never played a match?

1 (a) Can you name these two Leicestershire and England players?
(b) Who is the player making this extravagant gesture – and who is he doing it to? (*Answers on p. 97.*)

2 (a) Which member of Wales' most famous front row is missing? And who is his replacement?
(b) This all-Gloucester front row played together for England against just one country. Can you name it and them?

3 (a) Can you identify this outstanding international figure of the seventies?
(b) Four Lions on tour. Who and where are they, and what was unique about the visit?

4 Two well-known faces in unfamiliar jerseys. Can you name them, the teams they were playing for, and the occasions?

5 (a) Name the five upright All Blacks, and the Welsh No 7.
(b) What is the link between these two pictures?

6 Name these three England scrum-halves of the sixties and seventies.

7 (a) In which country did this international play his club rugby in 1985–6? And who is he?
(b) Who is this Australian scrum-half, and with whom did he form an outstanding partnership in internationals?

8 All four of these players captained their national side. Who are they?

Continued from p. 48

15 How did Daniel B. Carroll earn his place in rugby history?

16 The 1948 Wallabies were the first tourists to play against which British team?

17 Two New Zealanders played for Australia against the Springboks in 1971. Who were they?

18 Which Australian international won caps for which non-IB country before emigrating to Australia in 1984?

19 Which player scored a try in each match during Australia's Grand Slam over the Home Countries?

20 Who was the Australian outside-half who, in 1967 at Twickenham, became the first player to drop three goals in an international?

21 Which threequarters scored two tries when Australia lost to England 15–11 in 1982, and broke his arm during their 19–3 victory in 1984?

22 New South Wales toured France and the British Isles in 1927–8. Under what name did they tour?

23 In which year did Wales achieve their only victory in Australia?

24 The 1986 England v Wales game was refereed by an Australian controlling his first match between IB countries. Who was he?

25 In the IB Centenary celebration game between the British Lions and the Rest at Cardiff, both tries for the Rest were scored by Australians. Name them.

26 Australia's highest-ever score in an international was 37–12 in 1984. Against whom?

27 A flanker and a hooker hold the joint record number of caps for Australia. Who are they?

28 Who is the Australian forward who has scored a world record four tries in an international?

English & Welsh Cups

1 Which club appeared in the first five Welsh Cup finals, losing the first, then winning four in a row?

2 In 1986 this player became the first ever to score a hat-trick of tries in a National cup final.

3 The 1982 Welsh Cup final ended with a scoreline of Cardiff 12 Bridgend 12. Cardiff won the trophy because of scoring the only try. Who was the scorer?

4 Which club appeared in its first cup final when losing 25–17 to Bath in 1986?

5 In 1986 Bath became the second side to win three successive John Player Cup finals. John Palmer captained them in the last of the three – who was their captain in the first two?

6 Against which club in 1986 did Gloucester achieve a John Player Cup record score of 87–3?

7 Which club has only ever held the John Player Cup for just half a year?

8 What is the connection between the beaten finalists in the John Player Cup in the seasons 1973–4, 1979–80 and 1984–5?

9 Which club lost 18–12 against Bridgend when reaching their first and, up to 1987, only Welsh Cup final?

10 When he appeared for Barrow against Warrington in 1980–1 in Rugby League's John Player Special Trophy final, he became the first player to appear in both that competition and Rugby Union's John Player Cup. Who is he?

Over to Rugby League

1 St Helens paid a record fee of £25,000 for whom in 1979?

2 A member of the 1905–6 All Blacks side that toured Britain, he later returned and joined Wigan to become the first Commonwealth player to turn to Northern Union.

3 Two of the 1971 Lions turned pro. Who were they?

4 He played Union for St Helens and won four England caps in 1961, then played League for St Helens and won four Great Britain caps. Name him?

5 Another dual international holds the record for scoring most points in a Rugby League season. Who is he?

6 When Cardiff joined the Rugby League in 1981 they immediately signed three Welsh Rugby Union internationals who had played for Bridgend, Pontypridd and Llanelli. Who were they?

7 Who was the Neath prop who won 12 caps for Wales before turning professional with Widnes?

8 He equalled the Welsh individual try-scoring record with four against England in 1969 and 'went North' during the 1969–70 season. Who is he?

9 Having made his debut for Cardiff at the age of 17, he turned professional in June 1921 to begin what many people regard as the greatest career in Rugby League ever. Name him.

10 Which former Australian Union international was the leading points scorer in the Rugby League Test series against Britain in 1986?

11 Name the Australian member of a famous rugby family who scored in 11 successive games for Wigan in 1985–6, and was Man of the Match in the Lancashire Cup Final?

12 Which Irish international and British Lion joined Workington in the 1970–1 season?

Answers on pp. 100–1

South Africa

1 The British Lions drew a Test series in South Africa in which year?

2 Which Province won the Currie Cup for the fifth consecutive year in 1986?

3 Two forwards jointly hold the record for the most caps for South Africa. Who are they?

4 Which former Springbok captain became South African Ambassador to the UK?

5 Who holds the record for the most points scored in one international?

6 Who is South Africa's record points scorer against International Board countries?

7 Errol Tobias was the first black player to represent South Africa. Who was the second?

8 Which threequarter played 25 consecutive matches between 1967 and 1972?

9 Between 1973 and 1986 the Currie Cup was won by only two provinces, except in 1976. Who won it then?

10 Danie Gerber holds the record for try-scoring in internationals with 14, but which winger scored 12 tries between 1974 and 1981?

11 In which city is the Boet Erasmus Stadium?

12 Who scored 21 points for South Africa v The Rest of the World at Pretoria in 1977 and never played for the Springboks again?

13 Which club has provided the most Springboks?

14 Which back-row forward, born in Hertford and educated at Oxford, played twice against South America in 1984?

15 What skill is Danie Craven generally credited with inventing?

16 How did Philip Nel, captain of the 1937 Springboks, announce his retirement?

17 Who scored the only try against Wales at Cardiff Arms Park in 1951?

18 Only one point was scored against the first British touring team in 1891 in 20 matches. Who scored and how?

19 Who was the captain of the first South African team to tour abroad who told people to call his men 'Springbokken'?

20 In December 1985 two Springbok internationals moved to England to join Wigan Rugby League Club. Name them.

21 South African international outside-half Naas Botha had a spell in American gridiron football. He was employed as a goalkicker by which club?

22 How many different players did South Africa use in the four Tests against the 1974 Lions: (a) 25 (b) 29 or (c) 33?

23 During the British Lions' tour of South Africa in 1974, when they won three and drew one of the four Tests, only one South African scored a Test try. Who was he?

24 Who was the South African who scored tries in each of the first three Tests against the 1980 British Lions?

25 When England beat South Africa 18–9 in Johannesburg in 1972, which England player scored the only try, on his debut?

26 The South Africans lost 6–3 against Oxford University in the opening game of their 1969–70 British tour. On which ground was the game played.

27 Which player scored a hat-trick of tries when South Africa beat England by 35–9 in 1984?

28 Who captained South Africa to victory in the two Tests against England in 1984?

29 The 1955 Lions won the first Test at Ellis Park 23–22. Who was the South African fullback who missed a simple conversion in the last minutes which would have given South Africa victory?

30 How is the Springbok Head won, and who became the first winners of the trophy in 1912?

Rest of the World

1 Who captained Argentina in both internationals against England in 1981?

2 When he appeared against Leicester in 1979, he became the first Canadian to be selected for the Barbarians. Who is he?

3 The Barbarians came sadly unstuck in 1970 at Gosforth when they were thrashed 29–9 by which country?

4 Name the manager of the Japanese tourists who made his tenth tour as manager in England and Scotland in 1986?

5 The record score in an 'international' was set in 1979 at Oloron, when France defeated which country by 92–0?

6 Who was the Romanian whose try against Wales in 1979 gave his country a 12–6 lead before they eventually lost 13–12?

7 Ray Mordt has scored a record 34 tries for this nation.

8 Stefano Bettarello scored a massive 409 points to the start of 1987 for which national team?

9 Which African nation played in the Group 'A' of the FIRA championship between 1985–7 alongside France, Romania, Italy and the Soviet Union?

10 Who captained Fiji on their tour to Wales and Ireland in 1985?

11 Which country caused an upset by finishing ahead of Fiji and Tonga in the 1985 Pacific championship?

12 John van Altena was the first player to represent which country over 100 times?

13 The Alphaville Tennis Club were champions of which country on several occasions in the 1980s?

Answers on p. 102

14 Which national side, in 1939, became the first to tour New Zealand and return home unbeaten?

15 South African Izaak van Heerden became the first official coach of what country?

16 The 5,000 capacity Brondby Stadium is the headquarters of which country's Rugby Union?

17 Who suffered 56–12 and 82–6 defeats at the hands of Wales in 1975?

18 If Argentinians are Pumas, what are Americans?

19 Mark Wyatt played seven times at fullback for Wales in the early eighties. At the same time there was another international fullback with the same name. For which country did he play?

20 Which non-IB country beat England 16–0 in a Colts' International (under 19) in the 1985–6 season?

This and That

1 Who played on the wing for the Nile Club of Jinga in 1960?

2 The fullback in Rugby Union wears the No 15 shirt, but what number does his counterpart in Rugby League wear?

2 What are Ollie (S.O.) Campbell's christian names?

4 Michel Pomathios, winner of 22 French caps, became the first Frenchman to play for which British club?

5 Who refereed the first French Cup Final?

6 Faital Talpusi, Minister of St James' Reform Church in Sheffield between 1980 and 1983, captained which country at rugby?

7 Cliff Morgan played his last first-class game against East Africa in 1958. Which team was he playing for?

8 Which club fielded the first all women's team in the United Kingdom?

9 Gerry Lewis was the only member of the Newport club to go on the Welsh tour of Japan. What was his position?

10 The English Taylors was the first rugby club in which city?

11 Why was the Ireland v New Zealand game called off in 1966?

12 There have been seven Englishmen who have played in a Test match for the Lions without winning a cap for England, but only one Welshman who was never capped by his country. Who was he?

13 Which England cricket captain played rugby for Cambridge and Neath?

14 Sam Doble and Terry Cobner played together in which County Championship winning team?

15 What was unusual about the opposing captains in the 1937 Wales v Scotland international?

16 Where did England play their first home international in 1872?

17 Who is the heaviest man ever to play for South Africa?

18 Who or what is Wallis and Futuna?

19 Why could Billy Beaumont not get the attention of his players at half-time in the England v Australia match in 1982?

20 What is the Calcutta Cup made from?

21 Which two referees share the record for officiating in most internationals between International Board countries?

22 Albert Freethy of Wales was the last man to referee rugby in the Olympics. He also has a notable first to his credit. What is it?

23 Who is the longest-serving President of an International Board country?

24 In 1938 both Lions' fullbacks won 'Blues' for Oxford University. Who were they?

ANSWERS

England

1 Australia.

2 Tony Neary 43 caps, 1971–80.

3 Both against France. 1907 at Richmond 41–13; 1911 at Twickenham 37–0.

4 He scored a record five tries.

5 Eight: 1913, 1914, 1921, 1923, 1924, 1928, 1957, 1980.

6 1985. Wellington, New Zealand.

7 Taylor.

8 1973 (16–10). It was the only game they won on the tour.

9 He won three caps for New Zealand before beginning his England career.

10 W. W. Wakefield (later Lord Wakefield) 31 caps, 1920–7.

11 Wales. Blackheath, 1881.

12 He captained England to their only victories in South Africa (1972) and New Zealand (1973).

13 Mike Slemen – 31, 1976–84.

14 1963 (13–6), Richard Sharp.

15 12.

16 Ireland. 55 wins, 35 losses and eight draws to end of 1985–6 season.

17 The 1920s when they won four Grand Slams.

18 J. Heaton. Nine caps: three in 1935, three in 1939 and three in 1947.

19 'Dusty' Hare – 225.

20 Mike Harrison – in his first two appearances.

21 Dean Richards.

22 Andy Dun.

23 Gary Pearce.

24 Nigel Melville.

25 Bob Hesford.

26 Bill Beaumont.

27 Maurice Colclough.

28 Frank Prentice (1930).

29 Roger Creed.

30 John Horton.

Family Ties

1 Morne and Felix du Plessis.

2 Stewart and Jim Boyce.

3 Peter Brown was replaced by Gordon Brown (Scotland).

4 D. S. M. Macdonald (Scotland) D. A. Macdonald (South Africa).

5 Rodney and Richard Webb.

6 Don and Ian Clarke.

7 Gordon Waddell (1959–62), son of Herbert Waddell (1924).

8 Chris and Alan Old.

9 Finlay and Jim Calder.

10 Paul and Peter McLean.

11 Steve and Stuart Redfern.

12 Alan and Gary Whetton.

Questions on p. 13

All Blacks v Wallabies

1 Mark Taylor (Wasps).

2 Queensland.

3 Dave Loveridge.

4 T. C. Melrose.

5 Grant Batty.

6 Alan Sutherland.

7 John Thornett.

8 Rod Heeps.

9 Canterbury at Christchurch.

10 New South Wales.

11 Fergie McCormick.

Questions on pp. 14–15

Ireland

1 Mike Gibson (69), Willie John McBride (63), Fergus Slattery (61).

2 1948; Karl Mullen.

3 Jackie Kyle – 46 caps, 1947–58.

4 New Zealand.

5 G. V. Stephenson, 14.

6 Romania 60–0.

7 Syd Millar: 1962 and 1968 as a player, 1974 as coach and 1980 as manager.

8 Ollie Campbell (v Scotland 1982; v England 1983).

9 Cameron Michael Henderson.

10 Six: 1894, 1899, 1948, 1949, 1982, 1985.

11 Australia (won 6, lost 4, drawn 0).

12 Kennedy, eight. There have been seven Browns and four Brownes.

13 It was played on a neutral ground, Birkenhead Park. Ireland could not afford to travel to South Wales.

14 The home matches against Scotland and Wales were cancelled because threatening letters were sent to some of the visiting players.

15 Cork 1905; Belfast 1924.

16 No. In 1977 Phil Bennett and John Bevan, both from Wales, were the outside-halves. Mike Gibson joined the tour as a replacement threequarter but never played outside-half.

17 Limerick v Southampton in the UEFA Cup 1981–2.

18 Tony O'Reilly.

19 Trevor Ringland.

20 Willie John McBride.

21 Phil Orr. He won his 51st cap v Romania, beating Sandy Carmichael's record.

22 Trinity College Dublin.

23 Munster.

24 Tom Kiernan.

25 Shannon.

26 Tony Ward.

27 Church of Ireland Young Men's Society.

28 110 metres hurdles.

29 Cork.

30 On the wing.

Nicknames

1 Dai Morris (Wales 1967–74).

2 Gareth Davies (Wales 1978–85).

3 John Taylor (Wales 1967–73).

4 Pierre Albaladejo (France 1954–64).

5 Philippe Sella (France 1982–   ).

6 Robert Pararemborde (France 1975–83).

7 Bob Hiller (England 1968–72).

8 Peter Winterbottom (England 1982–   )

9 Peter Wheeler (England 1975–84).

10 Mark Shaw (New Zealand 1980–   )

11 Peter Whiting (New Zealand 1971–6).

12 Alex Wyllie (New Zealand 1970–3).

13 Gordon Brown (Scotland 1969–76).

14 John McLauchlan (Scotland 1969–79).

15 Iain Milne (Scotland 1979–86).

16 Matthys Michael Louw (South Africa 1928–38).

17 G. P. Lochner (South Africa 1937–8).

18 Philip Rudolph Van Der Merwe (South Africa 1981).

19 William Cerutti (Australia 1929–37).

20 Kenneth McMullen (Australia 1962–3).

21 Aubrey Hodgson (Australia 1933–8).

22 Roger Young (Ireland 1965–71).

23 Ray McLoughlin (Ireland 1962–75).

24 Jamie Salmon (New Zealand 1981, England 1985–   )

The Name's the Same

1 Robbie Deans and Colin Deans.

2 Mark Shaw and Tony Shaw.

3 Richard Harding and A. E. Harding.

4 Steve Smith and Arthur Smith.

5 Bruce Robertson and Ian Robertson.

6 Billy Wallace and A. C. Wallace.

7 Neil Bennett and Phil Bennett.

8 J. P. R. Williams and Bryan Williams.

9 Eric Evans and Gwyn Evans.

10 David Leslie and Andy Leslie.

11 Mike Weston and Lionel Weston.

12 Mike Gibson.

Scotland

1 Andy Irvine – 261 (includes a penalty try but excludes 12 points v Romania).

2 To the start of the 1986–7 season he had played 25 times on the wing without scoring.

3 Raeburn Place (home of Edinburgh Academicals) against England in 1871.

4 A butcher from Melrose, he invented 'Sevens' in 1883.

5 France. 27 wins, 27 losses and two draws.

6 New Zealand. 1983, 25–25.

7 Nine, 1938.

8 None of them have scored a try for Scotland.

9 It became the first of the Home Countries to defeat South Africa.

10 Ian McCrae (Gordonians) for Gordon Connell. France v Scotland 1969.

11 Ian McLauchlan and Gordon Brown.

12 I. S. Smith (v France and v Wales in 1925).

13 Gavin Hastings – 52, 1985–6.

14 44–0 v South Africa in 1951. A record between International Board countries.

15 Wilson Lauder (Neath).

16 He is the only Scot to have played for the Lions before his country. Four Tests v South Africa, 1924.

17 G. P. S. Macpherson.

18 Peter Brown.

19 Bruce Hay.

20 Sandy Carmichael.

21 Kilmarnock.

22 Ian McLauchlan.

23 Alex Brewster.

24 Jim and Bryan Gossman.

25 Dr Doug Smith.

26 Alistair McHarg.

27 Stewart's-Melville Former Pupils.

28 Alberta.

29 Heriot's Former Pupils (1978–9).

30 Edinburgh Wanderers.

Questions on pp. 23–4

All Rounders

1 C. B. Fry.

2 M. J. K. Smith.

3 Eric Liddell of 'Chariots of Fire' fame.

4 Nigel Horton.

5 Tony Harris.

6 J. P. R. Williams.

7 Gareth Edwards.

8 Brian McKechnie.

9 Martin Donnelly.

10 Jim Gregory (England), Ken Jones (Wales).

11 Charlie Faulkner.

12 Clive Van Ryneveld.

13 Kevin O'Flanagan.

14 A. E. Stoddart.

15 Sammy Woods.

16 Gary Knight.

17 Ian Balding.

18 Cyril Holmes (1947–8).

19 Jaco Reinach (capped against the Cavaliers).

20 They both captained Cambridge at rugby and cricket in the same academic year: Hignell 1977–8, Andrew 1984–5.

County Championship

1 Kent.

2 Notts, Lincs and Derby.

3 Graham Robbins (Warwickshire).

4 Durham.

5 Cheshire.

6 Bill Beaumont.

7 Gloucestershire.

8 Vale of Lune.

9 Staffordshire.

10 Peter Butler (Gloucestershire).

11 Barkers' Butts and Nuneaton.

12 North Midlands.

Wales

1 Phil Bennett – 166, the lowest total of the four Home Countries.

2 A. J. Gould – 18 (1889–97).

3 Haydn Tanner 1935–49, C. Howard Davies 1939–47, L. Manfield 1939–48, and W. Travers 1937–49.

4 They became the first club front row to play together for Wales and the British Lions.

5 Delme Thomas (v New Zealand in 1966) and Derek Quinnell (v New Zealand 1971). They also played together for Llanelli.

6 Keith Jarrett – 19 points (v England 1967).

7 16.

8 Malcolm Price (v Australia and New Zealand in 1959), J. J. Williams (v South Africa 1974).

9 Cliff Morgan – 29 caps, 1951–8.

10 Phil Bennett: one cap as replacement fullback, two at centre (one as replacement), one on the wing and 25 at outside-half.

11 The Joneses have it – 53. There are 50 Davieses, 40 Evanses and 40 Williamses.

12 South Africa.

13 1954, Scotland.

14 Gareth Edwards and Gerald Davies, 20 tries each.

15 Outside-half v England 1947 (the first official international post-war).

16 Bobby Windsor and Graham Price both scored on their debuts for Wales. Faulkner took four matches to score.

17 Most points for the British Lions on a tour. 188 in Australia and New Zealand, 1971.

18 The most points ever by one country in a Home Championship season – 102.

19 Jack Bancroft: eight v France, 1910.

20 Paul Thorburn.

21 Paul Ringer.

22 Clive Rowlands.

23 Flanker – v Australia 1978.

24 John Dawes – to Australia and New Zealand, 1971.

25 Terry Holmes.

26 Andy Hill.

27 By being named Man of the Match in the Welsh Cup Final.

28 Newport – they won 3–0 from a John (Dickie) Uzzell drop goal.

29 Ray (Chico) Hopkins, who also won a Lions 'cap' as a replacement for Edwards.

30 Steve Fenwick.

Captains

1 T. Hayashi.

2 Alan Philips.

3 Colin Deans.

4 Graham Robbins.

5 Paul Dodge.

6 David Leslie.

7 Daniel Dubroca.

8 Graham Mourie.

9 Andy Slack.

10 David Kirk.

11 Fergus Slattery.

12 Terry Cobner.

13 Cieran Fitzgerald.

14 Willie John McBride.

15 Les Cusworth.

16 John Rutherford.

17 John Perkins.

18 Andy Dalton.

19 Andy Slack.

20 Neil Macdonald.

All Blacks v Springboks

1 Laurie Prideaux.

2 Ray Mordt.

3 Naas Botha.

4 Andy Leslie.

5 Laurie Mains.

6 North-East Cape.

7 Kel Tremain.

8 Avril Malan.

9 Okey Geffin.

10 Theo Pienaar.

11 Rob Louw.

12 Don Clarke.

France

1 They were banned because the Home Countries considered them to be professionals.

2 J. P. Lescarboura – 54, 1983–4.

3 P. Albaladejo (v Ireland 1960), J. P. Lescarboura (v England 1985 and v New Zealand 1986).

4 They are the only two players since the war to score tries in all four championship matches in one season. Estève 1982–3, Sella 1985–6.

5 1979, second Test in Auckland. J. P. Rives.

6 R. Bertranne – 52 caps, 1971–81.

7 Benoit Dauga (50 caps: 29 at second row and 21 at No 8) and Walter Spanghero (42 caps: 21 at No 8, 16 at second row and five at flanker).

8 Pierre Villepreux.

9 Wales and England. France won 11–3 at Swansea in 1948, and 11–3 at Twickenham in 1951.

10 1978.

11 Venezuela.

12 Highest scores ever against Wales (23–15) and Ireland (29–9), their highest total points in a Five Nations Championship (98), and 13 tries equalling the record set in 1975–6.

13 They share the record for most internationals as captain – 30.

14 André and Guy Boniface; Guy and Lilian Camberabero; Walter and Claude Spanghero.

15 1910.

16 1959. Lucien Mias.

17 Jacques Fouroux.

18 La Fédération Internationale de Rugby Amateur (FIRA), which still organises a championship for non-IB countries in Europe and North Africa.

19 Béziers.

20 Argentina.

21 Pierre Berbizier.

22 Guy Laporte.

23 Benoit Dauga.

24 Michel Crauste.

25 Toulouse.

26 Racing Club, Paris.

27 Yves du Manoir. He died in a plane crash in 1928.

28 Guy Laporte.

29 Jacques Chaban–Delmas.

30 Agen.

British Lions

1 He played in every one of the 21 tour matches.

2 Bill Cunningham.

3 Argentina.

4 Sammy Walker.

5 Karl Mullen.

6 Doug Smith (1950 and 1971).

7 Tom Van Vollenhoven.

8 Mick Williment.

9 Bryan West.

10 He was the first replacement on a Lions' tour to the Antipodes, and it was made possible because he was the first Lion to fly there. The remainder travelled by boat.

11 In 1896 he became the first official replacement on a Lions' tour.

12 'Judge' Carl Aarvold, v New Zealand in 1930.

13 Stuart Lane.

14 Bob Hiller.

15 Gordon Brown.

16 Nigel Melville.

17 Robin Thompson.

18 Colin Deans.

19 David Watkins.

20 1980 to South Africa: eight.

21 Geoff Evans (London Welsh lock, 1971; Coventry centre, 1974).

22 Willie John McBride (17).

23 David Duckham; J. J. Williams.

24 Gwyn Evans.

Questions on pp. 38–9

Off You Go

1 Ross Cullen.

2 Nigel Horton.

3 Paddy Batch.

4 Cyril Brownlie (for New Zealand v England).

5 John O'Shea.

6 Keith Murdoch.

7 Dennis Burnett.

8 Mike Burton.

9 Peter Wheeler and Mark McBain.

10 Norman Sanson.

11 Jean-Pierre Garuet (1984).

12 David Chisholm.

The Changing Game

1 England.

2 Goal from a mark.

3 Roland Bertranne for France v Australia, 1972.

4 Neath in 1971.

5 One point.

6 *Tom Brown's Schooldays*.

7 Gilbert.

8 Colin Telfer for Scotland v France, 1972.

9 1969.

10 1969.

11 1948. Four points; Nim Hall (England v Wales, 1949).

12 Four: 1900, 1908, 1920 and 1924.

13 1895 (though the breakaway occurred in 1893 and the name Rugby League was not adopted until 1922).

14 1877 – 20.

15 a) 1897.

16 By a penalty shoot-out. The teams were still level after extra time.

17 Three (instead of two) players to form the front row.

18 1910. Billy Williams' cabbage patch.

19 Play the ball with his foot.

20 A kicker could place the ball himself for a conversion without using someone to hold it off the ground.

New Zealand

1 The 1924–5 All Blacks – played 30, won 30 (but they did not play Scotland).

2 Scotland and Ireland.

3 Most points on an overseas tour: W. J. Wallace, 230; most tries: J. Hunter, 42.

4 A. R. Hewson 26 v Australia, 1982. W. F. McCormick 24 v Wales, 1969.

5 J. C. Ashworth, A. G. Dalton and G. A. Knight: 20 appearances against IB countries.

6 C. E. Meads – 55 caps, 1957–71.

7 R. G. Deans of Canterbury.

8 South Africa has 20 victories, New Zealand 15, draws two (not counting 1986 tour).

9 D. B. Clarke – 207 points in 31 appearances.

10 R. M. Deans: 43 (three tries, 14 conversions and one penalty). New Zealand won 99–0.

11 B. G. Williams – 38 caps, 1970–8.

12 Taranaki in 1888.

13 In the third Test against the 1971 British Lions. He was recalled to play out of position in the second row. New Zealand lost 13–3.

14 By scoring a hat-trick against the 1983 British Lions in the fourth Test, to bring his tally to 19.

15 The 1983 All Blacks (v Scotland drew 25–25; v England lost 15–9).

16 Bob Burgess. He swallowed his tongue after a tackle in

the third Test in 1971 and Williams released it before he could suffocate.

17 No. They drew in 1928, but lost in 1949, 1960, 1970 and 1976.

18 Waka Nathan.

19 East Wales, who drew 3–3.

20 Colin Meads.

21 Kieran Crowley.

22 Auckland and Canterbury.

23 Alan Hewson.

24 Mike Gibson.

25 South Australia.

26 Doug Bruce.

27 Wilson Whineray.

28 Grant Batty.

29 Argentina.

30 He was the first back to captain New Zealand on a tour to Britain.

Places of Interest

1 St Helens, Swansea – Wales v England, 1882.

2 Twickenham. The first time a final was played there that did not involve a London county.

3 Welford Road, Leicester.

4 Liverpool – who have now amalgamated with and moved to St Helens.

5 Swansea – Wales beat France 49–14.

6 Whalley Range, Manchester.

7 Rugby . . . of course.

8 Queen's Club, London.

9 Murrayfield.

10 Inverleith.

11 Tahuna Park.

12 Kingsmead and Crusader Ground.

Firsts

1 Neath.

2 The first international in the United States – v Australia and lost 12–24. A match was played in 1974 v France but that was before the USRFU was officially formed.

3 United States.

4 Bledisloe Cup.

5 Middlesex.

6 Moseley (lost to Gloucester).

7 Arthur Smith, v South Africa 1962.

8 Llanelli.

9 France, 1900.

10 Colin Meads (NZ) in 1970.

11 British Lions, playing in the Jubilee Match.

12 Wales, 1908.

13 England v Scotland, from Twickenham.

14 R. L. Seddon, 1888 (A. E. Stoddart took over mid tour).

15 Guy's Hospital.

16 Prince Obolensky.

17 Broughton and Swinton.

18 He scored the first try at Twickenham.

19 A. H. Hornby. He captained England once at rugby, in 1882, and twice at cricket, in 1882 and 1884.

20 Pontypool, 1927 (v the Maoris and the Waratahs).

21 Malcolm Swain – for Moseley v Gloucester 1972, and for Aberavon v Llanelli 1974. He was on the losing side both times.

22 France, 1977.

23 Nim Hall (v Scotland 1947; v Wales 1949).

24 Australia 1947–8.

Australia

1 The McLean family. Doug Mclean began the dynasty when he played against the British Isles in 1904; his sons carried it on and the two Pauls (P. E. and P. W.), who played together in the late seventies, were the third generation.

2 Garrick Fay.

3 Ireland (16–3 in 1947 was Australia's biggest victory).

4 Sir Nick Shehadie.

5 1930 (6–5).

6 Steve Finnane, the Australian prop, broke his jaw.

7 Scotland (23–3) at Sydney in 1970.

8 There were five Tests.

9 They have both won five.

10 1965 when Australia won both Tests. They have lost to South Africa on every other occasion: two Tests in 1937, two in 1956 and three in 1971.

11 John Hipwell.

12 It made them Olympic Champions – Cornwall were nominated to represent Great Britain.

13 The Bledisloe Cup, donated by a former Governor General of New Zealand.

14 The 1939 Wallabies. War broke out and the tour was cancelled.

15 He played for Australia in the 1908 Olympic final and was in the USA team which won the 1920 final in Antwerp.

16 The Barbarians. They have played every touring team

to the UK since then.

17 Greg Davis and Bob Thompson.

18 Enrique Rodriguez, Argentina.

19 Mark Ella.

20 Phil Hawthorne.

21 Brendan Moon.

22 The Waratahs.

23 1969.

24 Bob Fordham.

25 Nick Farr-Jones and Simon Poidevin.

26 Scotland.

27 Greg Davis and Peter Johnson.

28 Greg Cornelson in the 30–16 win v NZ, 1978.

Picture Section – Answers

1 (a) Rory Underwood, Clive Woodward.
(b) Micky Burton – bowing to the England selectors after having been sent off in the Gloucestershire v Hertfordshire game, 1975.

2 (a) Charlie Faulkner; Glyn Shaw.
(b) South Africa, 1984 (1st Test) – Phil Blakeway, Steve Mills, Malcolm Preedy.

3 (a) Jean-Pierre Bastiat (France).
(b) Gordon Brown, Doug Morgan, Phil Orr, Steve Fenwick. On the first-ever British Lions' visit to Fiji, 1977. The Lions lost 21–15.

4 (top) Bryan Williams (NZ) playing for a World XV v England in the centenary game, 1971.
(bottom) John Rutherford (Scotland) playing for the French Barbarians v New Zealand at the Hong Kong Sevens, 1986.

5 (a) All Blacks (l. to r.): Ian Kirkpatrick, Bruce Murdoch, Tane Norton, Alan Sutherland, Jeff Matheson. No 7: John Taylor. Wales v NZ, 1972.
(b) With only minutes to go at the end of the 1978 game against Wales, All Black Frank Oliver (left) 'fell out' of the line and from the resulting penalty Bruce McKechnie (No 19) scored the winning points. (Final score: 12–13).

6 Mike Lampkowski, Peter Kingston, Bill Redwood.

7 (a) Italy; David Campesi.
(b) Ken Catchpole; Phil Hawthorne.

8 John Spencer (England) and John Dawes (Wales); Jacques Fouroux (France); Morne du Plessis (South Africa).

English & Welsh Cups

1 Llanelli.

2 Adrian Hadley (Cardiff v Newport).

3 Ian Eidman.

4 Wasps.

5 Roger Spurrell.

6 Exeter University.

7 Moseley. They shared it with Gloucester in 1982. (Gloucester won it outright in 1972 and 1978.)

8 London Scottish, London Irish and London Welsh – all exile clubs.

9 Pontypridd.

10 Ian Ball.

Questions on p. 59

Over to Rugby League

1 Clive Griffiths, who won a Welsh Union cap as a replacement against England in the same year.

2 Charlie Seeling.

3 John Bevan and Ray Hopkins.

4 Ray French.

5 David Watkins.

6 Steve Fenwick, Tommy David and Paul Ringer.

7 Glyn Shaw.

8 Maurice Richards.

9 Jim Sullivan (Wigan).

10 Michael O'Connor.

11 Steve Ella.

12 Ken Goodall.

South Africa

1 1955.

2 Western Province.

3 Frik Du Preez and Jan Ellis.

4 Dawie de Villiers.

5 Gerald Bosch; 22 v France, 1975.

6 Piet Visagie, 130.

7 Avril Williams (Western Province).

8 Syd Nomis.

9 Orange Free State.

10 Gerrie Germishuys.

11 Port Elizabeth.

12 Robbie Blair (five penalties and three conversions).

13 Stellenbosch University.

14 Nick Mallett.

15 Dive passing.

16 He threw his boots overboard as the team returned triumphant from New Zealand.

17 'Chum' Ochse.

18 Charles (Hasie) Versfeld scored a try – then only worth one point.

19 Paul Roos. Tour to the British Isles, 1906–7.

20 Rob Louw and Ray Mordt.

21 Dallas Cowboys.

22 c) 33.

23 Peter Cronje.

24 Gerrie Germishuys.

25 Alan Morley.

26 Twickenham.

27 Danie Gerber.

28 Theuns Stofberg.

29 Jack van der Schyff.

30 It is given to the first team to beat the Springboks on tour. Newport.

Rest of the World

1 Hugo Porta.

2 Mike Luke.

3 Fiji.

4 Shiggi Konno.

5 Spain.

6 Ionescu.

7 Zimbabwe (before moving to South Africa when Zimbabwe became independent).

8 Italy.

9 Tunisia (they beat Romania 17–15 in 1986!).

10 E. Teleni.

11 Western Samoa.

12 Holland.

13 Brazil.

14 Fiji.

15 Argentina.

16 Denmark.

17 Japan.

18 Eagles.

19 Canada.

20 Italy.

This and That

1 Idi Amin.

2 No 1.

3 Seamus Oliver.

4 The Barbarians.

5 Baron de Coubertin.

6 Western Samoa.

7 The Barbarians.

8 Percy Park.

9 Masseur and baggage master.

10 Paris.

11 Because of an outbreak of foot and mouth disease.

12 H. Poole. He won his Lions 'cap' against New Zealand in 1930.

13 Tony Lewis.

14 Staffordshire, 1970.

15 They both played for the same club: Edinburgh Wanderers.

16 The Oval.

17 Flippie Van Der Merwe – 20st 12lb (292lb).

18 It's a small rugby-playing island in the Pacific, affiliated to the French Federation.

19 A topless Erika Roe was distracting them.

20 Melted-down rupees.

21 Gwyn Walters and Kevin Kelleher.

22 The first sending-off in an international. Cyril Brownlie at Twickenham in 1925.

23 Dr Danie Craven (South Africa). He took office in 1958.

24 V. G. J. Jenkins (Wales), C. F. Grieve (Scotland).